THE POETRY GAMES

CHESHIRE & MERSEYSIDE POETS

POETS

Edited By Lawrence Smith

First published in Great Britain in 2018 by:

Young Writers
Remus House
Coltsfoot Drive
Peterborough
PE2 9BF
Telephone: 01733 890066
Website: www.youngwriters.co.uk

FOREWORD

Since 1991 our aim here at Young Writers has been to encourage creativity in children and to inspire a love of the written word. Each competition is tailored to the relevant age group, hopefully giving each student the inspiration and incentive to create their own piece of creative writing, whether it's a poem or a short story. We truly believe that seeing their work in print gives students a sense of achievement and pride.

For our latest competition The Poetry Games, secondary school students were given the challenge to stand up for what they believe in using nothing but the power of the pen. Using poetry as their tool, these aspiring poets were given the opportunity to express their thoughts and feelings on the topics that matter to them through verse.

Whilst skilfully conveying their opinions through poetry, the writers showcased in this collection have simultaneously managed to give poetry a breath of fresh air, brought it to life and made it relevant to them. Using a variety of themes and styles, these featured poets leave a lasting impression of their inner thoughts and feelings, making this anthology a rare insight into the next generation.

CONTENTS

Hannah Wasmuth (13)	72
Umme Rubab Kazmi (12)	73
Tristan Franks (12)	74
Jack Speakman (13)	75
Sam Rickers (11)	76
Olivia Hanna Benyon (11)	77
Nma Agina (13)	78
Eve Kayll (12)	79
James Knowles (11)	80
Billy Davies (12)	81
James Hale (13)	82
Matthew Hesketh (13)	83
India Grace Chapman (13)	84
Christopher Dutton (12)	85
Thomas Anderson (12)	86
Zuza Konca (12)	87
Hamish Scott-Herron (13)	88
Dan McFerran (12)	89

St Margaret's CE Academy, Liverpool

Boaz Paul (12)	90

University Of Chester Academy Northwich, Rudheath

James Dexter (14)	91
Ambrin Brown (12)	92
Liberty Hulse (12)	93

Upton Hall School FCJ, Upton

Alexandra Nicola Woodfin (15)	94
Grace Herd (12)	96
Sophie Anne Wolstencroft (15)	98
Rachel O'Flanagan (14)	99
Ruby Labone	100
Gabby Phelan	101
Aimee Barry	102
Amelia May Tweddle (12)	103
Taliya Campbell-Withe (13)	104
Zoe Killington (12)	105
Rosanna Blythe (11)	106

Jasmine Hothersall	107
Ella Niamh Owen (13)	108
Sarah Elizabeth Williams (12)	109
Merkita Quartey (12)	110
Tallulah Drummond	111
Kayla Grace Brandao (11)	112
Gabriella Kirby (12)	113
Penelope Murphy	114
Francesca Mairead Morgan (11)	115
Erin Whitehead (13)	116
Matilda Wootten (11)	117
Laura Whitehead	118
Alessia Saccucci (11)	119
Jasmine Sophie Clark (12)	120
Grace Swift	121
Maria Basanta	122
Harriet Dooley (11)	123
Sophie Higham	124
Eleanor Mary Curtis (13)	125
Jessica Doyle (12)	126
Lucy Jessica Jones (12)	127
Rebecca Fleming	128
Sophie Cotton (13)	129
Niamh Dyche (11)	130

THE POEMS

THE BEAUTY OF LOVE

From the day I opened my eyes,
I was *hungry!*
Hungry to know their names,
Hungry to know who they were.
I was striving to know whose family I belonged to.
Who would be my mother and father?
Who would take care of me?

As the days go by,
I realise I am the luckiest girl in the world.
Emotions flood through my veins,
My heart is warmed with love.
I wondered why this was only just happening to me,
Why was I feeling all of these emotions at once?
By the time I was able to read and write it came to me,
The reason that I had been wanting to know all of these
years,
The answer to all of my questions,
It's the *beauty of love!*

Courtney Louise Ridpath (11)
Beamont College, Warrington

YoungWriters Est. 1991

YOU WILL NEVER SEE ME AGAIN

Do you drown in your thoughts when the moonlight shines?
Or drown your guts in alcohol at later times?
Do you cry a river when the sunlight fades?
Or are you the reason someone cries alone for days?

Do you feel intimidated when I'm around?
Or do you intimidate others with your silent sound?
Do you feel a sensation when you erupt your words?
Or do you use them in a manner where no one is hurt?

Paranoid. Distressed. Breathless. Thoughtless.
With teary eyes I was left joyless.
Gone. Cold. Dead. Alone.
I'm hurt and scarred left for the unknown.

But you will never see me again,
Even when the pain will end,
You will never see me again.
You will never see me again.

Did you feel something there when you pushed me into the wall?
Or did you do it to show off to your friends in the hall?
Did anyone laugh with you when you spat in my face?
Or did you think that dragging me by my hair was ace?

Did you go home with red eyes feeling insecure?
Or did you beat me to the ground worse than before?
Did you leave school with tears on your cheeks?
Or were you the reason that someone was left in isolation
feeling weak?

Blunt. Distressed. Tired. Brittle.
I hated how you made me feel so little.
Frightened. Clueless. Deadly. Depressed.
You were nothing like the rest.

But you will never see me again.
Even when I've battled the pain.
You will never see me again.
You will never see me again.

Maya Greenwood (15)
Beamont College, Warrington

POETRY EMOTION

The more that you want it,
The more that you need it,
I always sense you by my side,
But now that you're gone,
I collapse to the floor and hide.

Switch off the lights, dim them down,
All happy emotions will unwillingly drown,
Nothing is out there that makes life worth living,
With an affirmative nature, there's nothing left in it.

The figure disappears, the fire slowly dies,
No longer does it matter, not even the lies,
And yet somehow you must still be there,
I pleadingly look up and drape down with despair.

By myself time and again,
Desperately asking myself when a new page can begin,
No matter how hard I could try to find,
Someone like you, I will permanently be denied.

How do they do it, put up with the truth?
I just fall to my knees in a lonely booth,
By myself now, forever alone,

Hoping that one day, you'll somehow come home,
I miss you.

Ethan Agrebi (12)
Beamont College, Warrington

LOST HAPPY ENDING

The moon opened his arms with fear,
As the apprehensive girl ran away as they were near.
Hastily she ran, hoping to be safe,
Wondering if she would find a better place.

There she was filled with fear,
As Jub roared, hoping they would disappear.
The tranquil forest lay very still,
As she sobbed, "Why me, why me?"

The feeble girl cried out with pain,
As the trees summoned the rain.
She looked up, took her final glance,
Evil figures were waiting to pounce.

Run Jub, run!
They are near,
They want you to disappear.
Run Jub, run, try your best,
But you won't complete your quest.

Faith Ratcliff (12)
Beamont College, Warrington

CIRCLES

I want to lie with you under dark skies,
but something takes your eyes off my blue eyes,
It makes my blood stop pumping and then on
the leaves fall grey, the water floods upon,
the shallowing sod, the mongrels, the cod,
until eyes stop catching, catching. Curst God.
Oh I can bleed and bleed and bleed and bleed,
as your new complexion is a new seed,
to catch new eyes and grow with the other floods,
to cage us in your ribs, to lock the doves.
You recycle away, away, away.
Who'd know you'd be at my feet to this day.
I'm warm, I'm alive, my heart was pure gold.
But you are broken, your heart is pure cold.

Evie-Gene Richards (15)
Beamont College, Warrington

DECAYING LOVE

Why love, something that will slowly decay,
Throughout the pain and sorrow, we begin to fray,
Like the fine fabric of a woolly winter jumper,
Until nothing remains of what was once there.

Love like a tooth, precious and prized
And important to lead a happy life,
However after time, neglect will wear it away,
Rotting slowly like love each day.

The painful realisation of hate and despair,
Broken, bleeding hearts plastered everywhere,
The red, burning flesh on our cheeks as we cry,
It's over, gone and time to say goodbye,
As eventually, everything we love or touch will somehow die.

Brodie McShane (13)
Beamont College, Warrington

MOMENTS

The moment I opened my eyes,
I was hungry... Eager to know their names.
One was missing,
Only one witnessed it.

Opening my eyes,
Opening them for the first time,
A bright glisten,
Before the face of my mother.

No father, no one but her,
He was elsewhere,
Doing something else,
Something he thought was more important.

Blank thoughts ran through my head.
Thinking of thoughts,
That were unbelievable.
Inventions that haven't even been made.

Unknown names...
Unknown places...
Finally being uncovered,
Unravelled to my eyes.

Joshua James Readon (12)
Beamont College, Warrington

IF

If I had a hammer, I would kill my family
And if I had a sailing ship, I would drown them in the sea
If I had a poet's hand, I would strangle them to death
And if I had the painter's touch I would take away their breath
But I don't have a hammer, but I do have a knife
And I don't have a sailing ship, but I can take away their life
I don't have a poet's hand but I do have some blades
And I don't have the painter's touch but I do have grenades
Aw, don't worry, there's no need to cry
Because right now it's your time to die.

Connor Heald (15)
Beamont College, Warrington

ALL THE WORLD WAS MADE FOR ME

Drifting over the untamed sea,
Nothing is as alone as me.
But there's nowhere I'd rather be,
Nowhere than the endless sea.

Dancing across the sea are wild waves,
Each a path they eagerly engrave.
When the wind fills my open sail,
Over the boisterous sea I prevail!

There's one thing only sailing does possess,
The thrills of flying over the wild wilderness.
I am a small boat meandering over the ocean,
My presence sets large waves in motion.

There are no bonds to bind me,
On the ocean I am truly free!

Laura Hughes (13)
Beamont College, Warrington

THE POETRY GAMES

Thank you for being the best dog you could
Thank you for being the cutest you could,
Thank you for keeping me safe all the time
Even when we are not together all the time

Every night I go to bed
I say something

I am so lucky to have you
You will always be in my mind
But most of all I thank you for being the funniest you could
You fill the house with laughter
Craziness and memories

There is nothing better than coming home to see you
Who will cheer me up when I'm down?
You, with your beaming eyes.

Abigail Hatton (12)
Beamont College, Warrington

INVINCIBLE

I committed suicide
I felt dead inside
But nothing hurt me before
Nothing can ever hurt me
Because I'm invincible

I've been shot by the FBI
They've killed me right inside
Nothing hurt me before
And I still can't die
Because I'm invincible

Life's a crime
A crime of misery
People fight
People argue
People have tried to hurt me
Life has tried to burn me
But I am invincible

Call me a superhero but I am not, I'm just me...
I'm invincible.

Dylan Lloyd Harrison (12)
Beamont College, Warrington

GEM OF JAPAN

A blooming rose,
A desert flower,
Open your heart's desire,
A sea of love washes over me
Come and sit next to me,
The gem of Japan is all that you see,
It's not what you think and it's not me,

If you enjoy the summer breeze,
Staring up at the stars in the midnight sea,
Then I will reveal to you what was revealed to me,
Beneath the busy town and streets,
A secret garden,
A gate of thorns,
Open to your deep devotion,
There you will find, what hides behind,
Japan's city voices.

Libby Ann Clarke (12)
Beamont College, Warrington

EMOTION

A wailing roller coaster of emotion,
Made up of commitment and devotion,
A boat to set sail far, far away,
As you will have to be prepared for a spiral of commotion,
But let's set it in motion,
Arguments can cause erosion
And that wailing roller coaster of emotion,
Once made up of commitment and devotion,
Once was a boat to set sail on far, far away,
Will no longer require the preparation for the commotion,
For your love will be torn apart,
Never forget the mark it made
And how she broke your heart.

Dillon Dearn (13)
Beamont College, Warrington

MYSTERIES OF LOVE

Why are we here?
To love, to lose.
Trapped in an endless maze of mysteries.
Where are we now?
When we are apart,
Your love for me dies,
But my love for you grows stronger.
Although your words cut me,
My love for you healed me.
Thump, thump! My heart mourns for our long-ended love,
An attempt to leap for you.
A silent commotion coursing,
A weed of evil to grow within us
And when the end of time is upon me,
My love for you will live on for eternities.
Why aren't we here?

William Griffiths-Dykes (12)
Beamont College, Warrington

YES

An unfamiliar spark,
Your destiny and fate,
Any time and anywhere,
It could come early but it's never too late.

Think of the opportunities,
The open gates and door,
One three-letter word,
Could be the cause.

The feeling of pride,
The satisfaction,
There is always a chance,
To make dreams come to action.

There is no wrong,
There is no right,
An idea, a dream,
A vision of light.

Maya Kuzma (12)
Beamont College, Warrington

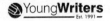

HORSES

Get on the saddle,
Hear the hooves clatter.
Trot along the grass,
Feel the wind go through your hair.
Carry on with a canter,
With a big cheery smile,
Ride on a steep hill,
Smell the hay from a horse's stomach.
Exercise your horse,
Jump over a gate.
Train your horse,
Go to a horse-jumping race.
Your journey is at an end,
You had so much fun,
Now pull the reins close,
Dismount your horse.

Lateishia Greenaway (13)
Beamont College, Warrington

GAMING

The world is crazy,
They think I am lazy,
My homework isn't done
Because it's not fun.

Everyone says it's late,
I'll start my homework at eight,
Now that I am in school,
I'll copy from anyone, even you!

So leave me alone,
I am going to stay at home,
Don't call or write,
I'm too busy tonight...

Kyle Antony Mckendrick (11)
Beamont College, Warrington

YESTERDAY

Yesterday, today and tomorrow
You will care for me
Through bad times and good times
You care for me
I hope you never leave my side
Because you are the best mum ever
Eleven years I have been on this Earth
And eleven years you have loved me
From the day I opened my eyes till the day I die
I know you will be good to me.

Madison Taylor (11)
Beamont College, Warrington

THE MAN IN BLACK

He helps the people. The poor and needy,
He defends them from evil and steals back what the army
stole,
He is the hero of the people,
He is a man of peace,
The only one who has courage to stand up for the people,
He fights for justice, he fights for peace,
The man in black, the only one who has courage,
The one true Zorro.

Dorottya Talaber (12)
Beamont College, Warrington

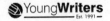

DO YOU HAVE TO GO?

Do you have to go?
You are the only one I know,
Gradually growing faint,
A bitter tear rolled down my face,

Painful thoughts crossed my mind,
Heartbreaking images crossed my eyes,
Nothing but silence,
The end is creeping near.

Leah Fraser (13)
Beamont College, Warrington

WAR

Fallen men, battered and bruised.
Explosions and desolation on the battlefield.
War, such a waste of life and time.

Destroyed cities, fire and rubble.
Buildings riddled with bullet holes.
War, such a waste of life and time.

Abandoned, smouldering vehicles.
Twisted lumps of metal as sharp as razors.
War, such a waste of life and time.

Broken families, loved ones lost.
Frightened and confused children.
War, such a waste of life and time.

Devastating, loss all around.
There is no going back, someone must have victory.
War, such a waste of life and time.

James David West (14)
Congleton High School, Congleton

WAR

The war has just ended and I am alive,
Just like the pictures that form in my mind.
The sound of the raging guns that shot men to the ground,
The cry of help that could not be found,
In the blanket of fog that lay around.
Falling and falling, the bodies formed a mound,
But no remorse could be found.
Asking around if we were homebound,
But again I was shooting them down.
We should not have a crown
for what we have found ourselves doing and doing again.
In the burial grounds of those who were proud,
The poppies grow around.

Hazel Ward (14)
Congleton High School, Congleton

VALUE HUMANITY NOT LIP SIZE

P ictures suggesting we should look a certain way.

E ndless changing how we look.

R ecklessly ruining our bodies.

F eeding ideas into our heads of how we should look.

E very day bullying others who aren't good enough.

C reating images in our heads of how we should look.

T aking it to the extreme to look a certain way.

I mpossible to be good enough.

O ver-the-top make-up and hair.

N o end to the way social media makes us feel.

Leah Eveleigh (14)
Congleton High School, Congleton

WHY I HATE MY HAIR

I went to get a trim,
The barber made it look grim,
My head is now cold,
I look dead old
And now the sides are slim.

Of that barber, I'm a hater,
My old hair was much greater,
My ears look like an elf,
I say to myself,
"Oh it will grow back later."

My hair is so bad, it's unfair
And no one seems to care,
But my lesson I've learnt
And some knowledge I've earnt,
I officially hate my hair.

Dan Walton (13)
Congleton High School, Congleton

WHO ARE YOU?

Who are you?
Social media sheep following the crowd,
Or are you yourself and of it you're proud,
You can be you,
That is true.
Be yourself
And have metaphorical wealth.
Being social media mad,
Isn't necessarily bad.
But it will get sad,
Just take a break,
It's a piece of cake,
"The youth are on their phones all day,"
That stereotype is so cliché,
Someone needs to save the day!

Kian Geoff Light (12)
Congleton High School, Congleton

UNTITLED

Our world is in destruction
A land of disruption
War after war
And yet still there'll be more
We act like we care
About our world that's in need
But really we just stare
And cowardly we plead
Countries get destroyed
Soldiers are deployed
To battles they didn't cause
And to wars they cowardly fought
And still we stare
And watch in despair
As our world dies
With nothing to spare.

Max Rigby (14)
Congleton High School, Congleton

5, 10, 33, 72, 612, 4.8 BILLION

5, the number of hours daily we spend on our phones
10, the age most parents give their children mobile phones
33, the percentage of toddlers who own an iPad
76, the percentage of people who text instead of meeting in person
612, the average phone bill per year
4.8 billion, the amount of people who own a phone

The phone

A device created to call
A device created to text
A device created to play games
A device created to take photos
A device created to browse the Internet
A device created to download your favourite apps
A device created to listen to music
A device created to watch movies

A device created to prevent you going outside
A device created to prevent you from talking to other people
A device created to stop you moving.

Olivia Wood (13)
Lymm High School, Lymm

ENDANGERED MAMMALS POEM

I'm black and white, I eat bamboo,
I lounge around all day,
However as my country grows and grows,
My habitat gets destroyed without a say:
The giant panda.

I'm black and fluffy; the mountain's my home,
I stay to protect my son,
But as the humans come closer and closer,
I'm faced with the end of a gun:
Mountain gorilla.

I can be grey or white, I have armour,
I love lying in the mud,
But the humans love my horn so much,
Then I'm killed and my horn goes *thud:*
The white rhino.

I'm dark grey, I love the mud,
I stomp around my territory,
But my tusks are treasured by the poachers,
They are used for ivory:
Asian elephant.

I'm white and stripy, I'm a big cat,
I love to swim and lure,
But my beautiful skin is very rare,
So therefore I'm killed for my fur:
Bengal tiger.

So now you know about endangered mammals,
Who are just dealing with it,
We shouldn't be the ones who are hurting,
So how would you like it?
Humans.

Grace Unworth (13)
Lymm High School, Lymm

STICKS

Into the classroom came running,
A student in absolute fear,
"A boy's come in with a stick!" he yelled,
"The boy I beat up last year."

"He says he's seeking vengeance
And that we will share his pain?"
My heart and mind were turned to ice,
At hearing these words yet again.

"It needs to end here," I said to myself,
As I stepped in the path of the stick,
"No one else should be hurt today."
His gaze fell on me double-quick.

"I'm sorry, what we did was wrong,
And that will never go away.
But if you could be the bigger man,
The cycle could end today."

"If someone hit me with a stick,
The pain would be intense,
But would the pain be any less,
If I hit back in defence?"

He put his stick in his holster
And shot me a menacing glare.

He spun on his heel and walked out of the school,
Leaving only a chill in the air.

Joanne Hewitt-Symonds (13)
Lymm High School, Lymm

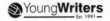

VOICES

In today's generation,
Our voices are ignored
And when we finally get to speak,
Someone always pushes out voices out.

In today's society,
Our voices are just silenced.
We are forced to wear clothes we hate,
Just to fit in.
We can't object, because at the end of the day,
People will hate you and bully you,
Just because you want to be unique.

But it's not just here,
It's around the world.
There are refugees out there,
Who are not let into our country,
People see them as dumb
And not worth their time,
But in the end,
The reason all these people are dying,
Is not because of their acts,
It's because of ours.

In today's world,
No one should be ignored,
Or have their voices silenced

We should be allowed to speak our minds
And to welcome others
Because after all,
We're human and we all deserve a chance.

Rachael Segal (12)

Lymm High School, Lymm

MY BROTHER WAS VERY HUNGRY

My brother was very hungry today,
He was not allowed breakfast,
The reason why, I cannot say,
He was thrown out the door,
He disappeared round the corner
And I didn't see him any more,

My tale now comes from a reliable source,
There is only one problem,
He only speaks in Morse,
I hear that he then went to school
He apparently said one plus one was four,
"Learn maths, you absolute fool!"

He then shoved his poem in his mouth,
My brother was expelled
And sent off heading south.
He still wanted food,
So he ate someone's sunflower,
That put the owner in a bad mood.

He found a washing line and ate somebody's pants,
It was very confusing,
She pondered it then blamed the ants.
I then found my brother

I am glad that he is okay,
The reason why, I can't say.

Joseph Chadwick (13)
Lymm High School, Lymm

MY LIFE

I'm Max
My inspiration is football
I play it myself
I even have a football
On the top of my shelf.

I can be very heartwarming
I can get very emotional at times
But that's just me
I love spending time with my family
And it sometimes goes on happily.

I like coming to school
For education and seeing my friends
But I get quite sad
Only when the day ends.

I like going to school because of my friends
Playing that game where everyone pretends
The friends are my favourite
But the fun never ends.

My favourite football team is United
My least favourite is City
But it doesn't really matter
Just like that goal from Juan Mata.

This is my poem that describes me
I'm really, really sorry
But I've got to go but only for tea.

Max Silvester (11)
Lymm High School, Lymm

A CITY FROM DAWN TILL DUSK

The skyline is a beautiful painting,
All different heights and lengths,
They stand there like soldiers,
Standing very straight.

The traffic is a bustling crowd,
Beeping to get past,
The hybrid of bright lights lures you in,
It could be a trap!

The streets are a large maze,
Winding here and there,
Every turn there is a surprise,
Waiting for you.

The billboards are like games,
Trying to beat you to it,
Their bright lights entertain you,
As you wander through the streets.

The shops are youth hostels,
That offer great things,
Souvenirs, fresh pastries,
Life's your oyster they say.

As the dusk sky turns to night
And the lights all go out,
The sun doesn't stay down for long
And then it's another new day.

Grace Unsworth (13)
Lymm High School, Lymm

MALICIOUS MASK

My mask
Clean and simple
An imitation of young culture
No Halloween costume
You dress up
Fit in
And fade

I'm short
That's not irresistible
Yet I stay true and play my schtick
No audience will clap
Or throw roses on the stage
Only an empty theatre
No exception
I did not fit in
An outcast

I fell to the ground
Discarded myself
And I locked myself away
Never to be seen again
No one wanted me

I'm selfish wanting attention
Lost to redemption

Yet I strive for acceptance
For an audience
For my drawings and art
But that theatre is closed
Flooded with blood
From my living heart
Would you care
Or would you leave me trapped in there?

Charlie Evans (12)
Lymm High School, Lymm

THINK

I wake up in the morning and think,
I think of all the animals who are out there,
Who don't have a drink.
Fifty-six billion animals are killed every year,
Fifty-six billion animals that are scared and full of fear.

Think of the rhinos, elephants, tigers,
Wolves, pandas, lions,
We are the fools.
We have made animals extinct,
What are we going to do?
I've got a solution just for you.
Killing them for their medication,
Horns and skin
Wasting their lives,
Putting the rest in the bin.

So next time just stop,
Just stop and think again,
If you were them,
How would you think and feel?

But you can stop it,
Saving their lives,
Next time just stop,
How would you like to die?

Roo Hornby (12)
Lymm High School, Lymm

AMMUNITION

Trembling, his fingers pulled the trigger
A deafening *boom* filled the air
Defending their country with great vigour
Men stand in heavy uniforms
As the smell of blood fills the air

Each with a set goal
Everyone thinking the same
Men dropping like flies
We hope you remember their name

Every man filled with regret
Shoulder to shoulder in a trench
Lice-ridden uniforms but no need to fret

Whilst no-man's-land looks lifeless
Men suffer much distress
With danger lurking round every corner
The sound of gunfire is a pest

As men watch their backs
Lives are lost every minute
Ammunition stored in stacks
Just wait till the gun is lifted

This is the war!

Katie Barnes (12)
Lymm High School, Lymm

THINK

Every day the same,
Cars, factories, smoke,
Always the same,
Nobody worried about our precious land,
Think.

A blanket of pollution,
Covers our atmosphere,
It's all our fault,
But nobody changes,
Think.

We carry on with our daily lives,
But far away from home,
Animals losing theirs,
We do nothing,
Think.

Land was colder,
Climates changing,
Lives ruined,
Will we ever change?
Think.

From once a quiet Earth,
To cars invading

Peaceful, too quiet,
We've done nothing to stop.
Think.

We've damaged the delicate crust,
There was no turning back,
Think of all the species we've lost,
What have you done?

Charlotte Toynton (11)
Lymm High School, Lymm

THERE IS SOMEONE IN MY HOUSE

Help me, help me,
There is someone here.
Breathing slowly,
Whispering things in my ear.

Is it a ghost,
Or maybe a mouse,
Creeping slowly,
Around my house?

Oh I know,
Maybe it's Santa,
Creeping slowly,
Just for the banter.

No it can't be him,
Maybe it's a pigeon,
Creeping slowly,
Around my kitchen.

No it can't be a pigeon,
Pigeons have wings.
Oh no it's a monster,
Messing with my things.

Help me. Help me,
Now I'm scared.
"I'm going to eat you,"
The monster declared.

I ran and ran,
Out of my house.
Then I realised it wasn't a monster,
It was in fact a little brown mouse.

Emily Anna Crouch (12)
Lymm High School, Lymm

SOCIAL MEDIA

The urge to gain more followers than him,
The need to get more attention than her.

But look more closely,
Look behind the filter and photoshops.
They are real people,
They have feelings.

Do you even know who you talk to?
Spending hours and hours in false relationships,
With people that are older or younger than you,
You don't know them.

How do you know you are not being stalked?
How do you know you are not being scammed by your
mates 'Colin' and 'Jeremy',
Who are actually hackers from Turkey.

Pay attention to who you talk to on social media,
Or it could end up bad.
You are responsible for what you do.

Will Day (13)
Lymm High School, Lymm

50

WHAT'S THE DIFFERENCE?

Why are we labelled since the day we were born?
Why does it matter whether we are straight or gay?
It should not matter! What's the difference?

Why are some people bullied for being disabled?
They are still human!
What's the difference?

Why does it matter what religion you are?
You still live a normal life!
Why should people care!
The answer to that is they should not.
What's the difference?

Why are we labelled, whatever we are:
Like Christian, gay, ADHD?
Why should we bully people when we probably are hiding
something ourselves?
Who wants to be labelled? Nobody!
There is no difference, that is the answer!

Niamh Johnson (12)
Lymm High School, Lymm

DEAR MR STRANGER

Dear Mr Stranger,
Before you judge let me introduce myself,
I'm not normal you see,
As my hair flows striding,
You sit there glaring,
Even if I'm wearing neon blue and yellow,
This is me but you keep on glaring.

Let me describe you,
A replica, a copy but we have seen it all before.
I almost feel sorry for you but I know...
I'm beautiful because I know my flaws
I'm strong because I know my weaknesses
And I am fearless because I learnt to recognise people like
you,
Who have nothing else to do but glare.

So next time you do so,
Just think how you would feel being glared at,
How would you feel, Mr Stranger?

Kathryn Eira Broadhurst (13)
Lymm High School, Lymm

HUMANITY

After all our time is over,
Everything is said and done.
We will realise the mistakes we made,
As totally immortal we become.

Only then will we see the error of our ways,
The mean and hurtful things we said.
That made a person feel so saddened,
As they rested their head for bed.

Only now, you see, do we remember,
The apology that we owe.
But as our time is nearly out,
There is no way that they will ever know.

So as you know, before we speak,
We should consider what's about to be said.
After all you're talking to a human being
And you will never know when they'll be dead.

Tegan Starkey (13)
Lymm High School, Lymm

A BEST FRIEND

B est friends are like stars, you don't always see them but you know they are there.

E ven though you have your fights you always come back to each other.

S ometimes you just need a shoulder to cry on.

T hrough the years you have never grown apart.

F riends will always be there for you but never like your best friend would.

R ealising you have each other's backs is the best feeling ever.

I f they are happy so are you.

E ven on your darkest days, they shine a light for you.

N o one has ever seen you apart.

D ays wouldn't be the same without them.

Isabelle Rogers (13)
Lymm High School, Lymm

VICTORY

We soldiers were in a muddy trench,
No food and no water,
The armoury full of guns and grenades
We were planning for over the top at 6am...

Bang!

What was that?

It was a grenade!
Get down!

It killed ten men
Injured many more
Our plans ruined
Our lives ruined
On that day
It all went downhill.

Then, before the break of day,
We attacked where the Germans lay
After a few minutes,
It was all over.

They had surrendered
And all that day
All we heard was...

"Victory! Victory!"

Adam Williams (12)
Lymm High School, Lymm

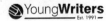

WAR

Why do we all fight each other,
When you could be at home helping your mother?
Bullets zooming across the sky,
When we could be with our fathers eating pie,
Bang! Bang! Bang! the bullets go,
As soldiers run to and fro,
Cowering in those dirty trenches,
When we could be mingling with those Frenchies.

Blood spattered all over the floor,
When we could be helping out the poor,
Why can we never have any peace,
But constantly get in trouble with the police.

I know this is deep and all of it is true,
Why should we be fighting against me and you?

Matthew Beattie (12)
Lymm High School, Lymm

THE HORRORS OF WAR

People falling all around,
Gunfire causing a deafening sound,
Bombshells destroying all to be found,
Some experience nothing more,
Nothing more than the horrors of war.

Bullets tearing through the air,
Explosions showing off their fiery flare,
The abundant moans of despair,
Everyone hopes for something more,
Something more than the horrors of war.

Fatally injured, accepting their fate,
PTSD leaving broken men in its wake,
Each faction feeling immense hate,
We all wish for anything more,
Anything more than the horrors of war.

Ben Bower (13)
Lymm High School, Lymm

COMING OUT AS GAY

Have you ever been bullied to submission,
With no one there to listen?
You roll up in the situation, scared
And you feel like you're the only kid living,
In the solar system prison,
You hope you weren't there.
But let me tell you that this story isn't about me you see,
It's about a boy who just wants to let his feelings free.
But someone came along and told him not to.
He cried and sighed every day,
But I picked him up and told him,
"You're going to be okay."
You should never be afraid of coming out as gay.

Lucy Newall (13)
Lymm High School, Lymm

WHO ARE YOU?

Dementia is something that changes your life,
You don't remember anything, even your wife,
They try to tell your family it will be alright,
Then you start to go walkabout at night.
Memories go blurry, your life is a mess,
You want to be resting in God's swallow nest.

As for your family, they worry about you,
They don't want to lose you.
Your freedom is taken,
You'll never remember the sweet smell of bacon.
Your coat is gone from the hook where it stayed,
Please, this is not the end, save him, we prayed.

Hannah Craven (12)
Lymm High School, Lymm

ANIMALS ARE JUST LIKE US

Animals are just like humans,
Except they look different,
Trying to find food, shelter, water,
But most importantly trying to survive.

Animals are not evil,
They are independent, strong and fight for their habitat,
Some bright and vibrant, some dark and dull,
Some scaly and slimy, some furry and dry.

Some animals can be vicious and violent,
But there is no right to kill them,
They fight to protect, they die to save others.

They are just like us humans,
Except they kill other animals for a reason...

Lizzie Lloyd (12)
Lymm High School, Lymm

SAVE THE ENVIRONMENT

Ice caps are melting,
Whilst polar bears are yelping,
Yelping in starvation.

The creatures in the sea,
Used to swim happily,
But now we destroy their homes
And even some that roam.

Hear Mother Nature's shout,
Whilst there's pollution all about.
Whilst we burn fossil fuels,
Not realising we are being cruel,
As we cut down trees,
Say goodbye to a fresh clean breeze.

Recycle and reuse,
Are words we all know,
However we never use them
And that has to go.

Amber Agar (13)
Lymm High School, Lymm

BELIEVE

Stand out from the crowd,
Don't hide in other people's shadows.
Be who you are inside,
Don't try to hide yourself.
You can do anything if you really put your mind to it,
You only have one chance.
If you woke up twenty years in the future
And you didn't do as well as you could have done,
Would you regret it?
Just think about that.
All the power is in you,
So don't sit back.
Push yourself to the limit,
Aim for the stars and you will reach them,
Believe in yourself...

Nathan Brown (13)
Lymm High School, Lymm

DEATH

The painful feeling of your last breath,
The stressful feeling of being chased down by Death.
It gets you in the end...

Isolated spirits rapidly moan,
From under their worn-out gravestones.
It gets you in the end...

Tragically dead children aged not much younger than seven,
Certainly off to luxurious Heaven.
It gets you in the end...

Villainous villains that have nothing to dwell,
Have only a one-way ticket down to the pits of Hell.
Death will get us all in the end.

Benedict Tyzack-Smith (12)
Lymm High School, Lymm

ROAD TO WIMBLEDON

It's match point, before you serve,
You see the trophy, you know you deserve,
You bounce the ball a couple of times
And clear negative thoughts from your mind,
You release the ball into the air,
With lots of concentration in your stare,
You smash the ball into the corner of the box
And the ridiculous force blows off the other player's socks,
The moment of relief,
One of disbelief,
You finally lift the Wimbledon prize,
An emotional glimmer in your eyes.

William Andrews (12)
Lymm High School, Lymm

OCEAN EYES

Open your eyes and see the light,
Not your phone but the world.
Oceans wider than Kim K's butt,
Mountains with a higher streak than you and your friend,
Creatures that are more beautiful than Kylie Jenner.
Explore the world,
Climb those mountains,
Open your ocean eyes.
Don't let a small brick,
Define and control who you are.
A phone can hold you back from:
A world,
A place,
A home,
So look to the world,
Open your ocean eyes.

Laura Antrobus (12)
Lymm High School, Lymm

MY GRANDAD

My story is about someone who lost a leg
Chose his country
And fell before the disease of madness

My story is about people who were cowards
Who were courageous
Who murdered

My story is of guns
Of hope
Of despair

My letters contain
Broken promises
Tears of love
And clinging hope

My memories remember
A smile
A laugh
And the person who did many things
My story is of the person I call my grandad.

Freya Rain Jackson (12)
Lymm High School, Lymm

THE BULLY

The bully is angry,
He feeds off your fear,
He wants you to tremble,
Whenever he's near,

A bully is angry,
She's pressured inside,
Whenever she see you,
She wants you to hide,

But the bully doesn't hate you,
They're only upset,
The hatred inside,
Will go, you can bet,

Because the bully feels emotion,
Just like you and me,
So if you give your time to help them,
They'll change you will see.

Mai Beetham (12)
Lymm High School, Lymm

I ONCE DREAMED A DREAM...

I once dreamed a dream,
Where the world was fine,
People were good
And worshipped the saviour divine.

Peace, there was everywhere,
Nothing else to declare,
Murderers, rapists, all in the wrong,
Had come to place where they belong.

Pollution had stopped,
Deforestation too,
Everyone loved one another
And the beautiful things that they do.

I once dreamed a dream,
On the bed where I lay,
Evil had ended in every way.

Clare Davis (13)
Lymm High School, Lymm

PEOPLE

I am English,
You are Chinese,
I am American,
You are Russian,
I am South African,,
You are from Brazil.
But we're the same!

We are girls who love life and live for tomorrow,
We take opportunities
And if we get stuck along the way,
We'll make something of it.

But we are divided by race and language,
By what country we call home
And what we have and don't have.
But we're the same!
We are people!

Amy Deeks (11)
Lymm High School, Lymm

MY WONDERLAND

The past is the past they say
Just wait for the next new day
As the wasted days go by
I try to remember my wonderland

Where everyone is equal
We don't need a sequel of the world we live in today
Where women are as strong and powerful as men
And black people and white people are treated the same
again

There are no constant wars
And no rich or poor
Where animals are free
And we are happy
In my wonderland.

Rebecca Whitehead (12)

Lymm High School, Lymm

ALL ABOUT LIFE

There are those who let their friends do the work
There are those who do everything
Those who are nasty
Those who are nice
Those who take opportunities
Those who leave them
Those that are lazy
Those who are exhilarating

There's carers
There's sharers
There's exciting
There's dull
There's nastiness
There are victims
There's laughter
There's sadness.

Fletcher Hewitt-Dutton (12)
Lymm High School, Lymm

THE ENDING

It's life-threatening
An evil act on those with insecurity
But, they have a heart that beats
Just like yours
They are no different

Many people take in the pain and hate differently
It's an evil of age, war and hate

Bullying
It should never happen
But it happens a lot
It may have happened to you
Just think who are you hurting?
What will be result at the end of it?

Hannah Wasmuth (13)
Lymm High School, Lymm

THE WORKING BEE

Flash of yellow,
Flash of black,
Buzzing past, what's that I hear?

Working away,
Throughout the day,
Nestling in flowers and enjoying the rays.

Returns to the hive,
Tired and sleepy,
All covered in pollen and full of nectar.

Having done the last waggle dance,
Shakes off the day's work,
And settles down for tomorrow's another day.

Umme Rubab Kazmi (12)
Lymm High School, Lymm

LONDON TO EDINBURGH

London, King's Cross, full of steam,
The locomotive fuelling up preparing for departure,
The signal's up, the regulator's open, London is behind.
Peterborough gone in a blink of an eye.
Up the East Coast, Newcastle and then the Scottish border's bridges,
Inverness, Edinburgh, through the ridges
And behind us now here Stow Fen's tunnels,
Until, at last, stopped.

Tristan Franks (12)
Lymm High School, Lymm

WAR

War is violence and pain
It isn't just a game
What will the world become
If everyone uses a gun?
How much do the people have to pay
Their homes, their country and sent on their way
Is there any hope?
How will they cope?
Is killing the answer?
What chance is there?
Trained to protect or kill
To serve a ruler's will.

Jack Speakman (13)
Lymm High School, Lymm

HOME

As I run into the treacherous trench,
A bullet races past my head,
I hear the general bellowing orders at us,
When really, I want to go home,
But I can't,
Yelled at, shot at, this is not the life I wanted.
I don't want to die,
Not like this.
I need my home, I want my home,
Is this the end, the end of me and my family?

Sam Rickers (11)
Lymm High School, Lymm

HOME IS ANYWHERE

Home
Home isn't a place on a map
Home isn't four walls
Home is a place in your heart
A place with memories and meaning
Home is a place to share with family and friends
Home can be a country, a town, a street, anywhere
Home isn't a place you come to every day
It could be a place you see once a year
Home is anywhere.

Olivia Hanna Benyon (11)
Lymm High School, Lymm

WHEN WILL IT END?

Seventeen dead, chapters unread, constant dread,
Endless killing, people begging, life losing,
Triggers pulling, fingers trembling, life vanishing,
When will it end? Oh another fifteen dead, people seeking
revenge,
Alive one minute, dead the next, undeserved last breath,
Put the gun down, no hesitation, it just could save this
generation.

Nma Agina (13)

Lymm High School, Lymm

CAT

Creeping, crawling, silent cat
Starting to wonder where you're at

All the time you snore and snooze
But never down with the blues

Your friends lurk in the garden
Always begging for your pardon

But still don't move your lazy backside
Lying next to the fireside.

Eve Kayll (12)
Lymm High School, Lymm

SPORT IS FUN

Sport you can do anywhere,
From running to football,
Rugby to gymnastics,
Handball to cricket.

"Why do sport though?" you ask,
Sport is fun that is why,
Sport also makes you healthier,
Sport exercises your mind.

Sport is fun and good for you.

James Knowles (11)
Lymm High School, Lymm

BULLYING

Bullying should be a crime in our society.
Bullying could say bye-bye to people.
Bullying is no way to treat people.
Bullying can cause bad things for people.
Bullying can put blood on your hands.
Bullying can put people behind bars.
We need to stop bullying.

Billy Davies (12)
Lymm High School, Lymm

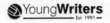

SOCIAL MEDIA

Social media,
Hiding behind a curtain,
But who are you?
No one can be certain,
Hiding behind an Internet wall.
Bringing yourself up and making others fall,
Shaming on Instagram, bullying on Snapchat,
Why do we do it? Let's stop all that.

James Hale (13)
Lymm High School, Lymm

EYES

Eyes,
They are the spark of skies,
The dawn of days,
They turn life upside down,
To an easy view,
A deciding view,
There is no limit,
To the way you see life,
You are different,
You are normal,
But you just don't see it.

Matthew Hesketh (13)
Lymm High School, Lymm

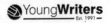

FOREVER SILENCED

Today they stomped in
Future's forever in the bin
Reputation's tainted
After all this time?
Ruining all they've created
Students come to school to learn and play
But how are they supposed to do that
If you won't put that gun away?

India Grace Chapman (13)
Lymm High School, Lymm

WORLD CUP

The World Cup 1966,
The only success England have ever had
Yet we're all so passionate about it,
What about all the people that have never seen a football,
Millions spent on players,
But nothing spent on prayers,
Are we aiming for the right goal?

Christopher Dutton (12)

Lymm High School, Lymm

EARTH

(Haiku poetry)

Earth is full of life
Creatures that are great and small
Are passing away

We don't admit it
But we are murdering Earth
All life receding

We're choking the Earth
Leading all life to an end
You can help stop it.

Thomas Anderson (12)
Lymm High School, Lymm

INVISIBLE PAIN

In the thunder
In the rain
In the lightning
In the pain

You are strong
But you are weak
You are loud
But you won't speak

You can do it
I know you will
You'll get to the top
You have the will.

Zuza Konca (12)
Lymm High School, Lymm

WHO ARE YOU?

Who you are?
Why do you care what other people think?
You are you.
You should be yourself and that makes you.
You can be whoever you want to be.
You should never be influenced by anyone but yourself.
Who are you?

Hamish Scott-Herron (13)

Lymm High School, Lymm

DIRT

Dirt is good, dirt is great
Dirt is all over my plate,
I love dirt as dirt loves me,
We are one big family,
Where I go dirt will always be there to give me a hug,

I love you, dirt.

Dan McFerran (12)
Lymm High School, Lymm

BATTLE OF THE BULGE

As the days grew longer
The more we had to suffer
As battle raged on
The Germans weren't gone

The deadly bullets flew past
But we weren't as fast
The evil shells didn't come to a stop
All our hope seemed to be lost

The allies slowly paralysed in fear
There the casualties were very severe
Little did they know help was near
Their faces looked truly sincere

The Germans realised the trouble they were in
They quickly fled with a spin
Nothing would be won here
But bodies will be there only as a souvenir...

Boaz Paul (12)
St Margaret's CE Academy, Liverpool

CRIME AND RHYME

There once was a boy who wanted to rhyme
All he knew was a life of crime
He laughed at life and didn't care
Went around with a vacant stare

So he went to the teacher and said
"How can I rhyme? Get it into my head."
She said, "Stop the crime, clear your thoughts,
Do some good deeds, take a pause."

He walked away with his head in his hands
Knew she was right, time to make a stand
Stopped the bad and brought in the good
Time to get out of the brotherhood

Took pen to paper and gave it a go
Felt really good just goes to show
Now his life is happy and bright
All along the teacher was right

Good prevailed over time
Now he writes and it's *rhyme, rhyme, rhyme!*

James Dexter (14)
University Of Chester Academy Northwich, Rudheath

THE BULLY

Why me?
Why anyone?

My mind is locked
In a prison of emotions
Each word chains me to the cell
The way I look doesn't change me
Yet, you won't leave me alone

The voices inside my head are swayed to your side
They beat me down
Day after day
It won't stop

I am scared to tell
They will scar me till the end
What's the point
It won't leave me alone

And still I ponder
Why me?
Why anyone?

Ambrin Brown (12)
University Of Chester Academy Northwich, Rudheath

WOMEN'S EQUALITY

(A kennings poem)

Debate igniting
World enhancing
Mind empowering
Confidence boosting
Job designating
Sexism banishing
Economy growing
Independence creating
Strength increasing

I am women's equality and I will not be defeated!

Liberty Hulse (12)
University Of Chester Academy Northwich, Rudheath

THAT EXTROVERTED BOY

There was a girl named Lucy,
She didn't talk that much.
No one really knew why,
It's just how she grew up.
She bottled up all her problems,
Until they broke her down.
People just chose to avoid her,
Nicknamed her 'freak of the town'.
Since Lucy was a quiet girl.
She didn't say a word.
She didn't give them a piece of her mind,
Her voice was never heard
One day, Lucy met a boy,
The extroverted type,
He laughed and sang and spoke all day,
To her he was just right.
She cherished him with all she had,
She never did give up.
She told him all her hopes and dreams,
She truly was in love.
To him she was still the freak,
The girl with the messed-up mind

But to her he was everything,
Sweet and thoughtful and kind.
Oh, how she thought she'd found the one
Oh how she jumped for joy.
Oh how she loved him with all her heart,
That extroverted boy.
The mask the boy put on for her,
Was one made out of pity,
For he did not believe she was kind,
Or sweet or thoughtful or pretty.
She cried and cried for days on end,
Begging him to think twice.
The only thing he said to her was,
"My love comes at a price."
Lucy tried her best to keep him,
But it never was enough.
After all the price to pay is high
When it comes to love.
There was a girl named Lucy,
Oh, how her heart was broken.
Poor Lucy's hopes and dreams were crushed,
Yet not a word was spoken.

Alexandra Nicola Woodfin (15)
Upton Hall School FCJ, Upton

PERFECTION

Why can't I look like her?
A stunning pale complexion,
Blush rosy cheeks,
Luscious strands of dark hair,
Plump red lips.

Why can't I look like her?
A perfect tall figure,
On every magazine,
Soft brown eyes,
Looking straight through mine.

Why can't I look like her?
If I look at her too long,
I feel I can't eat,
At a possible chance of looking slightly like her,
I become emaciated.

Why can't I look like her?
For me it's not an option,
It's not physically achievable,
To look like a person, they are not themselves,
In my heart I know it's fake.

Why can't I look like her?
Pixels are subtracted from her natural beauty,
Leaving thousands of girls comparing their features

To someone they will never be,
Whether big or small, tall or short,
Every girl is *perfect*.

Grace Herd (12)
Upton Hall School FCJ, Upton

THE MENTAL ENEMY

A deadly beast stares at you viciously in the eye,
Its deadly fists wrapped tightly around you,
Refusing to let go!
A gruesome war is occurring in your influential brain,
The bloody battle raging between whether to continue
Or run away in defeat!

Trembling,
Your frostbitten fingers lean forward,
The cool, soft object touches your skin,
A poisonous stench rises up and floods your senses.
Frantically,
Your brain explodes into horrifying images,
Warning of the grotesque monster that will invade you!
Rapidly, the fearsome enemy approaches!
Taunting your fragile brain
as it storms the barricades of your deprived lips,
Deadly substances slither down your throat,
Collapsing in the depths of your stomach.
Standing triumphantly,
You revel in the fact you have defeated 'Ana'
Once again.

Sophie Anne Wolstencroft (15)
Upton Hall School FCJ, Upton

INSIDE OURSELVES

You would rather let a human freeze,
Than let them cross a line,
Innocence slowly dying,
Along with our humanity.
We would rather have our nails and hair done perfectly,
As if such a thing exists,
Than let a man eat.
Your weak terrified minds bring us brutality and war.
Your greedy wicked hearts bring us a hateful society.
Turning all those good hearts away
While their hearts remain frozen,
But not the ice of the Arctic.
We call two humans holding hands disgusting,
Yet we stay silent,
Afraid to say anything,
When we see a man holding a gun.
Shooting at our humanity, destroying the freedom
And putting them in fear,
But we pray...
We are searching for peace and pleasure
Tearing apart lives and homes,
Memories and humans.
Yet we don't look inside ourselves.

Rachel O'Flanagan (14)
Upton Hall School FCJ, Upton

WHY?

Why do you bother?
Why do you bother to continuously berate me?
I sit in my room waiting for another traumatising comment
to come through.
Why?
How do you live with yourself?
How do you live with yourself when you know that you're
tearing someone apart daily?
How?
Imagine it's you
Imagine it's you, the one who receives the horrid messages.
How would you feel?
Imagine.
So next time think about what you're doing.
But the thing is, there won't be a next time.
You won't bother to continuously berate me.
You won't bother to tear someone apart.
You won't imagine being the one who is receiving all of
those horrid messages.
You know why?
Because I won't let you bother.
I don't say why any more, I say bye.

Ruby Labone
Upton Hall School FCJ, Upton

WICKED WAR

In terrible times of war,
We must remember those who have died,
To save our precious lives.
They have sacrificed themselves,
In order to save the world.
In hope that one day peace will come,
And happiness will be for everyone.

They pray one day the world will change
And turn away from its wicked ways.

The bombings and wars ravage many lives,
And those who survive will become refugees,
No shelter to hide.
Their homes destroyed with nowhere to go,
They search high and low
Then all hope is lost,
What is the cost?
Our fellow humans living in fear,
Just because the war is here.

The world must change its wicked ways,
And in the end we all will pray,
That peace will come for everyone.

Gabby Phelan
Upton Hall School FCJ, Upton

ANIMAL CRUELTY

There is no reason for animal abuse
They are suffering every day
There is definitely no excuse
For making innocent animals pay

It's happening all over the place
People do this way too much
This is a really serious case
Imagine the animals' soft touch

Nothing deserves to be treated this badly
Clear tears trickle down
I would stop this forever gladly
A beautiful smile turns into a frown

Fuzzy fur turns into stone
This poor animal turns cold
This animal is definitely not alone
As this sad story is heartbreakingly told

I write this poem to show
That doing this is so low
And if you do this just know
That you should really just go.

Aimee Barry
Upton Hall School FCJ, Upton

NATURE'S END

The dog
Starved, beaten, locked away,
I probably won't eat today,
My tail hung low,
There is nowhere to go.

The elephant
My beautiful tusks stolen from me,
How harmed a creature like me can be,
Left unable to defend myself,
As my tusks will be displayed on a shelf.

The leopard
They chase me as they want my fur,
Soon I will be left cold and bare,
A creature like me will soon be in the past,
As they continue to hunt us, we cannot last.

The polar bear
Ice disappears from under my feet,
Soon I will have nothing to eat,
As the icy water creeps in,
I know this is a war I can't win.

Amelia May Tweddle (12)
Upton Hall School FCJ, Upton

EXISTENCE

Hi my name is Cancer,
I can't speak to you, you can't see me,
I can rush down your veins and you would never know,
The bigger I grow, the more you die and the weaker you get,
I didn't choose you for a reason,
I guess I just got stuck with you,
Basically I'm like a really needy friend;
Except I'm not your friend,
I don't care who you are,
Or what you do,
Or how you look,
All I need is a body to grow in and that's you,
I was waiting for the right conditions to try to exist,
At some point you sat in front of a microwave for far too
long,
Or maybe you got hit with a bad case of DNA,
But it was all I needed to exist.

Taliya Campbell-Withe (13)
Upton Hall School FCJ, Upton

A WORLD FULL OF HATE

We all want a peaceful world
Where everyone has a mate
But it is only one big dream
We live in a world full of hate

People having to leave their homes
War ruining their lives
Not enough clean water or food
It's a desperate struggle to survive

They must flee their country
To escape the dreadful war
Missing their old lives
They want to return once more

Living in fear
Hoping it will end
Children living with strangers
Wanting to make a new friend

We all want a peaceful world
Where everyone has a mate
But it is only one big dream
We live in a world full of hate

Zoe Killington (12)
Upton Hall School FCJ, Upton

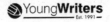
DO YOU CARE?

Animal cruelty, when will it end?
For tired tigers and their friends,
Pandas, elephants and polar bears,
Their lives destroyed.

Do you care?

Not just on land, but in the sea,
Giant squid, whale sharks, we're their enemy.
They struggle to live in the depths,
We've led these poor creatures to their deaths,
Their lives a ruin.

Do you care?

Hunters, poachers, they're out every day.
Illegal killing, it's not the way,
The planets get polluted,
Let's do something now,
Our generation can figure out how.

Do you care?

Rosanna Blythe (11)
Upton Hall School FCJ, Upton

HOMELESS

Hungry, cold, sad and left,
Cold floor and no bed,
Alone left waiting for love,
To be given from God above.

You have a warm house and a chunk of money,
Whilst I am sat here cold and hungry,
You walk in the shops and spend your wages,
Just walking past me, been sat here for ages.

The winter has come, the season of snow,
Cold again and lonely,
Sat alone on Christmas Day,
No food and nowhere to stay.

You open presents, gifts galore,
I'm still sat here on the floor,
Not one present for me alone.
Receiving a gift would be the
Best memory I would own.

Jasmine Hothersall
Upton Hall School FCJ, Upton

NORMAL

I smile but I'm not okay
This grin is fake
And so is the personality I make
I feel trapped, feel alone
I have no one to speak to
But this cannot be shown

People pretend to care
But they don't
They want to 'help'
But are too scared, so won't
Everyone seems normal
Happy as can be
Calm and relaxed
So why can't that be me?

One day I'll be happy
I promise you that
My face will be pretty
And my tummy, flat

Oh, why can't I be normal?
It's in my dreams
But this will never happen
So it seems...

Ella Niamh Owen (13)
Upton Hall School FCJ, Upton

I BELIEVE

Why do you treat us differently?
Who has the upper hand? Me, you, that woman over there?
It isn't fair!
Times have hardly changed, nobody has.
I will make a change, I will fight all day and night.
Nobody will tell me no!
People say I shouldn't be here, too young to know about the past,
Well, I say I can see the future and it doesn't look so bright.
I'm not a fake, I'm not a mistake, it's all set in my DNA.
You can't and you won't change my mind!
I will help people and stand up through the nights,
I believe in equal rights!
Never give up!

Sarah Elizabeth Williams (12)
Upton Hall School FCJ, Upton

ALONE

I'm weak so weak I can barely move,
But if she asks me, I'll have nothing to prove,
I'm broken inside hurting so badly,
Every time I walk, I move so sadly.

But who can I talk to? There's no one there,
I'll tell my parents but they won't care,
They'll give me a glare and say stop being a moaner!
But I have no friends, I'm a loner.

I tried to stand up,
But I'm as flimsy as a paper cup,
So I crouched into a ball
And started to call.

Help me! Help me! Is somebody there?
But who am I kidding? Nobody cares.

Merkita Quartey (12)
Upton Hall School FCJ, Upton

MY BLOOD IS RED

Although we are not born racists,
Racism has always been around,
Symptoms are: feeling that you are bound
And you cannot turn around.

I may be treated differently because I am not Caucasian,
I may be Aboriginal, East Indian, African or Asian,
The colour of my blood is still red,
The colour of my skin comes from my origin.

So how can we blend colour, creed and race?
By joining our hands
And looking face-to-face,
Believing we are all equals,
Thinking that everything is fair
And that God holds us in His hands,
Very dearly.

Tallulah Drummond
Upton Hall School FCJ, Upton

LIFE BEHIND SOCIAL MEDIA

There is a life beyond our lives,
Which seems to always draw our eyes,
Where Snapchat and Facebook seem so fun,
But behind the screen it's really dumb.
What's the bother trying to hide?
When you're really beautiful in and outside,
Some people 'act' extra nice,
But on the inside they are as cold as ice.
When adults are children
And children are adults.
People will trick
And take a pick
On vulnerable, innocent, young children.
This is the end of my story,
So you should be careful, surely?

Kayla Grace Brandao (11)
Upton Hall School FCJ, Upton

WHAT IF?

Trapped, suffocated,
My fragile mind reaches out,
But doesn't quite make it...
What if? What if? What if?

Sly, devious,
Hiding in plain sight,
Do I need to wear a mask?
What if? What if? What if?

Dangerous, descending,
I'm a time bomb,
Waiting to go up in a puff of smoke,
What if? What if? What if?

Treacherous, alone,
I can run,
But there's nowhere left to hide,
What if? What if? What if?

Why should I be neglected?
What if I was just myself?

Gabriella Kirby (12)
Upton Hall School FCJ, Upton

THE INTERNET'S TWISTED WAYS

Her face is pale,
Body weak,
She is dying for something to eat...

Still her body doesn't look like theirs,
It's a thin hollow frame,
Skin draped everywhere.

She lets out a tear,
It cascades down her ghostly face.
Is this living? she contemplates.

Another day goes by
And so does another meal,
What is fake and what is real?

She tells herself she's done,
All because of the Internet's twisted ways,
Another person who will be missed for days.

Penelope Murphy
Upton Hall School FCJ, Upton

MIRROR IMAGE

I look in the mirror
And what do I see?
Somebody I don't know,
Staring back at me.

She is all skin and bones,
Her cheeks are hollow.
If she doesn't eat,
Something worse will follow.

I look in the mirror
And what do I see?
An imperfect body,
Standing in front of me.

Her face is round,
She is plump,
She actually believes,
She's a worthless lump.

This shouldn't happen,
It isn't right.
For this issue,
We should fight.

Francesca Mairead Morgan (11)
Upton Hall School FCJ, Upton

UNTITLED

Why does he not care?
Why is she never there?
Why does he always drink?
Why does she always shout?
Why does he hit me?
Why does she kick me?
Why don't they care?

I feel scared,
I feel like no one cares,
I feel shaken when they hit me,
I want them to go,
When I go to sleep at night,
I imagine,
Imagine I have parents that actually care,
But when I am about to meet them,
I stop,
Their piercing screams deafen me,
I can't take it any more.

Erin Whitehead (13)
Upton Hall School FCJ, Upton

EQUALITY

Vast and strong is childhood,
Though some might neglect and dishonour it.
White, black,
Why do our colours collide?
Rip apart,
Selfishness and cruelty wraps its sleekness inside us.
The baby cries with all his might,
No one is there to save and cherish him.
Far away his white mother lies as she leaves
Her black beauty behind.
In her green eyes, pure green evil resides,
Eating away into her ugly, weak soul.
Don't judge people by their skin colour or appearance.

Matilda Wootten (11)
Upton Hall School FCJ, Upton

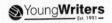

ALL ON SOCIAL MEDIA

All on social media,
Everyone in the world.
We're empty, sad, plain and obsessed
With numbers, followers and more.

All on social media
Is where most bullying takes place,
Mean and cowardly,
Brutal and cruel.

All on social media,
Where we're pressured to look perfect.
We can't wake up with bed hair
Or have a single blemish.

All on social media,
Which is just to communicate,
Show off; look good or worse,
To bully...

Laura Whitehead
Upton Hall School FCJ, Upton

I'M AUGGI CARTMAN

I'm Auggi Cartman,
I'm normal but different,
People slowly kill me,
They torment me,
They berate me.
Why?
It never brings me down,
I'm my own superhero,
I'm the artist to my own canvas,
Remember when I said that I was different?
Well, I'm proud of it.
There is nobody else like me.
Yes, I may look like a Picasso painting,
But I will say it loud and clear!
I'm Auggi Cartman!
The only one in the entire world.

Alessia Saccucci (11)
Upton Hall School FCJ, Upton

THE ENVIRONMENT

Save the trees, save the money,
Think about the bees who give us honey,
Remember that Amazon rainforest? Thought not!
And all those rabbits that hopped,
They've been hunted and are now dead,
Like all the rest covered in blood, red.

Car fuels leaked into the air,
With fossil fuels everywhere.
The polar bears have no home,
To live or breathe or to own.
So future generations let's make a pledge,
To make this world the very best.

Jasmine Sophie Clark (12)
Upton Hall School FCJ, Upton

THE HORRORS OF WAR

Bang! Bang! Bang!
The horrors of war,
So scared we flee,
It does not resolve,
Remains unsolved.

Bang! Bang! Bang!
Our hearts beat rapidly,
Here one minute,
Gone the next.

Bang! Bang! Bang!
Here we go again,
War ruins the innocent,
Creates endless dismay.

Bang! Bang! Bang!
Don't despair,
War will end,
Come what may,
Let's fight for change today!

Grace Swift
Upton Hall School FCJ, Upton

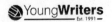

OUR PLANET NEEDS US!

I would like to apologise to the world
Or better said to future generations.
For not having enough trees to breathe oxygen,
Or to make our planet more beautiful.
Sorry for killing all the trees,
To make money to build a rocket,
And launch it into space to find a new home to live on,
Instead of taking care of our own.
We failed you, we failed the planet,
I have a voice and so does nature and so do you!

Maria Basanta
Upton Hall School FCJ, Upton

WHEN WILL IT STOP?

When someone asks me,
"What's wrong?"
I simply reply with,
"I'm just tired,"
And they agree.

But you see this exhaustion,
It's not something that is resolved by sleeping.
I can't simply shut my eyes and wake up okay.

I just want it to stop,
I can't handle it any more,
I need a break from my brain,
My heart.

Harriet Dooley (11)
Upton Hall School FCJ, Upton

WAR

The night fell dark and I'm far from home,
I'm in the trenches all alone.
More rain and rain comes pouring in,
Whilst I think about where I've been.
I think of my family, mum and dad,
About how they must feel so very sad.
Dark clouds turn red,
The injured and dying lie in sickbeds.
As their faces turn pale as chalk,
They lie there now unable to talk.

Sophie Higham
Upton Hall School FCJ, Upton

EARTH

Stilted, poisoned and dying
I beg you to stop
My heart aches, I'm crying
I beg you to stop

My heart chokes with plastic waste
My brain running round with the constant thought
Of litterbugs all over the world
I stop and think
Does it have to be this way?

Day by day it gets worse
So *stop*
You are slowly killing me.

Eleanor Mary Curtis (13)
Upton Hall School FCJ, Upton

THE BULLIES

Sweat begins to cake my face,
As they start to chase me.
They pick up the pace as they come to face me.
Coming closer and closer still.
With fear I begin to fill.
My heart skips a beat,
I fall to their feet,
They are the predator, I am the meat.
When something else rose up inside me,
A new-found strength that wouldn't hide me.

Jessica Doyle (12)
Upton Hall School FCJ, Upton

I WANT CHANGE

Are you a black person?
Or are you a white person?
No matter what,
We are all equal,
Girl or boy?
Want to be the other?
Thin or fat?
No one cares if you're either,
In the end,
We all should be kind.
No matter what,
We are all loved the same,
As we all breathe
And move in some way.

Lucy Jessica Jones (12)
Upton Hall School FCJ, Upton

NOBODY

I am a refugee,
I am black,
I have no education,
I can't find a job,
The NHS won't fund my needs,
People spit on me as they walk past,
I was once surrounded by bombs,
My family is gone,
Paper is being scattered on the floor like it's nothing,
No one will listen to me,
I am nobody.

Rebecca Fleming
Upton Hall School FCJ, Upton

BULLYING

B ad things are happening

U se your brain and do something

L ies are being spread

L ies are wrong

Y ou will overcome

I solated and alone

N ot knowing what to do

G rowing up not being confident.

Do not bully, it's wrong!

Sophie Cotton (13)
Upton Hall School FCJ, Upton

SOCIAL MEDIA

I was cyberbullied,
All about the way I looked
And who I am,
They called me names of many kinds,
Texting and talking,
No stop at all,
Echoes of laughter,
Stuck in my head,
I need help,
Please now!

Niamh Dyche (11)
Upton Hall School FCJ, Upton

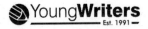

YOUNG WRITERS INFORMATION

We hope you have enjoyed reading this book – and that you will continue to in the coming years.

If you're a young writer who enjoys reading and creative writing, or the parent of an enthusiastic poet or story writer, do visit our website **www.youngwriters.co.uk**. Here you will find free competitions, workshops and games, as well as recommended reads, a poetry glossary and our blog.

If you would like to order further copies of this book, or any of our other titles, then please give us a call or visit **www.youngwriters.co.uk**.

Young Writers
Remus House
Coltsfoot Drive
Peterborough
PE2 9BF
(01733) 890066
info@youngwriters.co.uk

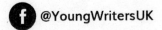 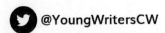